D0279839

First published in the UK in 2009 by Little Star Creations,
an imprint of Holland Publishing PLC.
18 Bourne Court, Southend Road,
Woodford Green, Essex, IG8 8HD.

www.littlestarcreations.co.uk

Designed by: Lavish Productions

Printed in China

Cute little rhymes about
love
The
Pet Poets
Club™

To all our lovely owners
Who think that we can't speak
Who think we only bark and growl
Miaow, or squawk, or squeak

We do indeed have voices
We use them all the time
At the legendary Pet Poets Club
The home of rhythm and rhyme

Cute little rhymes...
for those special times

LOVE

I felt I really had to say
I think about you every day
And to show how much you mean to me
Here's some very cute pet poetry

Puppy Love ♥

They told us it was puppy love

When we first met each other

But this love that we share

MAKES US FEEL SO YOUNG

That we will be puppies forever!

The Perfect pair

Everyone who sees us
Says we make the perfect pair
The bond between us grows each day
Through this love that the two of us share

I hope it doesn't sound too soppy

But thinking of you

Makes me feel so

HOPPY!

I really should have

told you sooner...

I love you much,

much more than tuna!

I may not be clever
Wealthy or witty
But you have to admit
I'm one fine-looking kitty!

My heart ♥ belongs to you

Everybody loves me

But I'll never be untrue

You can see it my big, bright eyes

My heart belongs to you

I know I've got some
emotional baggage
But I love you
even more than cabbage!

Rabbits love carrots

Budgies love Trill

But I love only you

And I always will!

We must be in love
What else could it be
That makes my heart sing
When you're perched next to me?

This could be the day
When you meet the one
Who banishes grey skies
And brings out the sun

I love you,

love you,

love you so

(As if you didn't already know)

Heaven Sent ♥

Snuggled in your nice warm lap
I'm so happy and content
This love between the two of us
Is surely heaven sent?

The Sunday roast
I love the most
Is of course...
Lamb (with mint sauce)

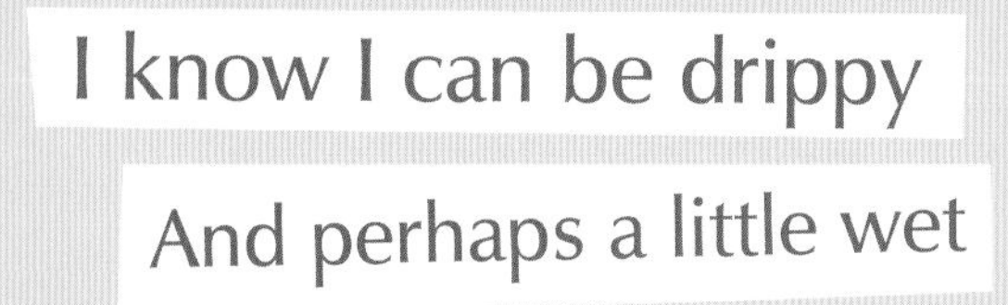

But the first time that I kissed you

Is something I'll never forget!

Dear ♥
Husband...

To my wonderful husband

You're the love of my life

You truly have made me...

...the HOPPIEST wife!

Pussycat, pussycat, where have you been?

I've been dying to tell you

That I'm really quite keen

Pussycat, pussycat, what do you say?

We'd be perfect together

So let's seize the day!

Irreplaceable

Some people seem to think I have
A funny little face
But I know you think I'm beautiful
And impossible to replace

I'm sure this is a moment

That you wouldn't want to miss

Me all fluffed and ready...

And waiting for a kiss!

The world seems such a perfect place

Each time I see your perfect face

A gift from above

Little puppies truly are
A gift sent from above
Wagging tails that say 'Hello'
And eyes brim full of love

You're absolutely perfect

So clever, smart and sassy

...and so much fun to have around

What a bonny, little lassie!

Ginger girls are gorgeous

Black girls are terribly sweet

White girls really float my boat

And grey girls look a treat!

I'm dotty ❤
about you!

I'm sure it isn't hard to spot...

That I really love you

Really a lot!

It's fantastic that you love me

Despite my 'funny ways'

Even when I'm looking ruff

On my slightly 'dog-eared' days

The Sunday roast

I love the most

Would have to be...

Beef, for me!

My Purrfect Wife ♥

I just wanted to say 'I love you'

You've completely changed my life

Ever since that day you purred 'I do'

And became my wonderful wife

You make me feel like I'm walking on air

I see your smile everywhere

I'm sure it isn't hard to tell

That I'm caught within your magic spell

The day that I set eyes on you

My lovely little kitten

Was the day that I became

Well and truly smitten

I will always be your little pup

Even when I'm big and all grown up

I love you

You always take such care of me

I'm always warm and full

Every little thing I need, you give

And I love you for it all

It's time for us to say goodbye
We thank you for your time
And hope to see you back again
At the home of rhythm and rhyme

Titles in the series: